Piano
Grade 4

Pieces & Exercises

for Trinity College London examinations

2012-2014

Published by
Trinity College London

Registered Office:
4th floor, 89 Albert Embankment
London SE1 7TP UK

T +44 (0)20 7820 6100
F +44 (0)20 7820 6161
E music@trinitycollege.co.uk
www.trinitycollege.co.uk

Registered in the UK
Company no. 02683033
Charity no. 1014792

Printed in England by the Halstan Printing Group, Amersham, Bucks.

Allemande in A minor

HWV 478

George Frideric Handel
(1685-1759)

Dynamics are editorial. Chords may be arpeggiated on the beat.

Rondo

2nd movement from Sonatina in F, Anh 5

Ludwig van Beethoven
(1770-1827)

Dynamics and articulation in square brackets are editorial.

4

(3) Players with small hands may omit the bracketed notes.

5

Allegretto

from Sonatina in G, op. 55 no. 2

Friedrich Kuhlau
(1786-1832)

(*1*) Players with small hands may omit the bracketed notes.

Kaki-no-Tane

Akira Yuyama
(born 1932)

Composer's metronome mark ♩= c. **152**.

Solfeggio in F

K. 393 (385b) no. 2

Wolfgang Amadeus Mozart
(1756-1791)

Dynamics are editorial.

Sicilienne

no. 11 from *Album for the Young* op. 68

Robert Schumann
(1810-1856)

A Sad Story

no. 6 from *Thirty Pieces for Children* op. 27

Dmitri Kabalevsky
(1904-1987)

[Blank page to facilitate page turns]

Tapping Heels

Alan Bullard
(born 1947)

Composer's metronome mark ♩ = *c.* **84.**

Never Too Late

Heather Hammond

Composer's metronome mark ♩. = **50**.

Exercises

1a. Fun and Games – tone, balance and voicing

1b. Solemn Melody – tone, balance and voicing

2a. Floating High, Sinking Low – co-ordination

2b. Scuttlebugs – co-ordination

21

3a. Open Spaces – finger & wrist strength and flexibility

3b. Moving In Closer – finger & wrist strength and flexibility